ADVANCED CARTOONING
AND OTHER DRAWINGS

B. Kliban

Andrews and McMeel

A Universal Press Syndicate Company

Kansas City

ISBN: 0-8362-1710-1

Library of Congress Catalog Card Number: 92-74805

────────── ATTENTION: SCHOOLS AND BUSINESSES ──────────

For B. Kliban
1935-1990

E Ke Aloha, Welína Kāua

I Ke Aloha

J.K.K.
1993
Hana, Maui

Introduction

Here is a selection of some of the vast work of B. Kliban—a tall, kind man known to his friends as "Hap," because he was born on New Year's Day.

He was an art school dropout, a beatnik with a drawing pad, who left the East Coast for San Francisco, and sold his first cartoon to *Playboy* for $25. He was a man who loved cats and pasta puttenesca and hated lawyers and pine trees.

Trying to describe Hap's work is like trying to answer the Japanese journalist who asked him, "Explain to me, strange humor."

What can you say about "Turkish Vibrating Soup," "Better living through plywood," "Ship in Zucchini," or "An idea destroying itself by perception."

What can you say to explain a cartoon of a man sitting in a jail cell with the sun shining through the bars, staring at the shadow on the wall, but the shadow has no bars? Or what about a waiter approaching a customer in a restaurant and saying "Eggplant Parmesan? I thought you wanted some Toyota headlights"—except that it's funny.

If I had to pick out one cartoon that best portrays Hap Kliban, it would be one he drew of a cave man standing on the edge of the earth throwing rocks at the stars. And second would be the cartoon of the long-haired man sitting on a bed of nails saying, "It only hurts when I exist!"

Hap threw rocks at the stars. And he did much better than march to a different drum, he drew to it.

Don Novello
San Anselmo, California
February, 1993

Sitting Around the Laughing Stick

Iglamids

4

THINGS TO DO IN NEW YORK - *Eating Oysters out of a Shag Rug*

Taxidermy

EVERY ONCE IN A WHILE TED COULD STICK HIS FOOT
INTO ANOTHER DIMENSION,
BUT HE NEVER KNEW WHICH ONE.

"PUT YOUR MONEY ON NUMBER FIVE," MURMURED THE SWARTHY MIDGET TO FRED'S HIP,
WHILE OUT ON THE TRACK THE GRANDMOTHERS SNORTED AND PAWED THE TURF,
EAGER TO REACH THE PILE OF APPLIANCES AT THE FAR END OF THE OBSTACLE COURSE.
"WHOA, YOU GRANNIES!", KIDDED THE PUBLIC ADDRESS ANNOUNCER, TO THE AMUSEMENT
OF MUCH OF THE CROWD, MANY OF WHOM WERE EXTREMELY LIMITED IN INTELLIGENCE.

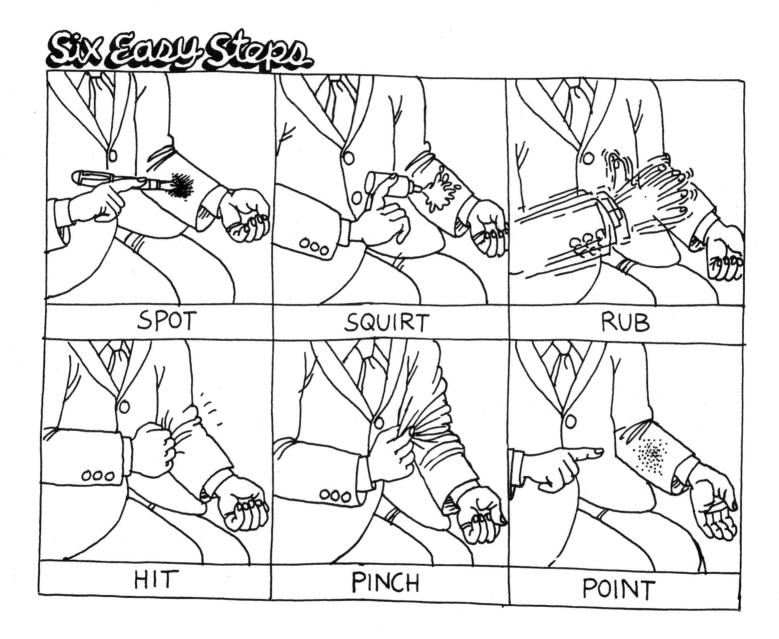

13

CUDS OF THE OLD WEST

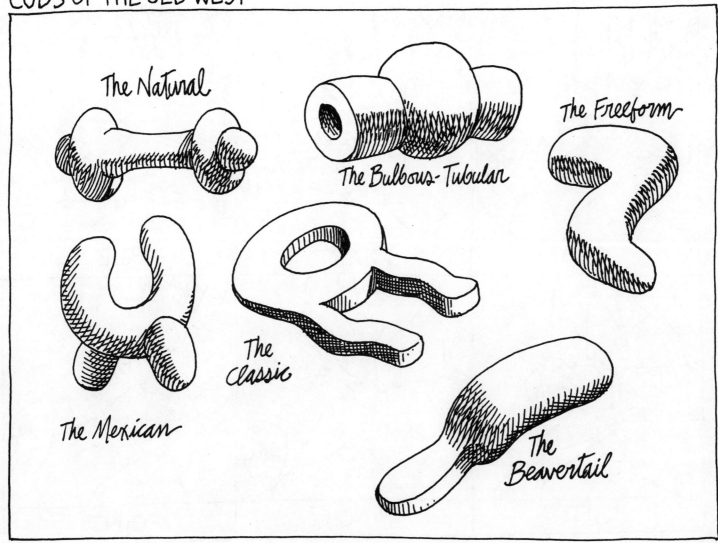

Cubists and Their Wives

Life is Just a Bowl of Mutated Cherries

The Farmer

Chromium Oxhide

NO MATTER HOW MANY TIMES YOU DRAW A BANANA,
IT WILL ᵁˢᵁᴬᴸᴸʸ NEVER BE A BANANA.

22

24

Two Amusing Water Tricks

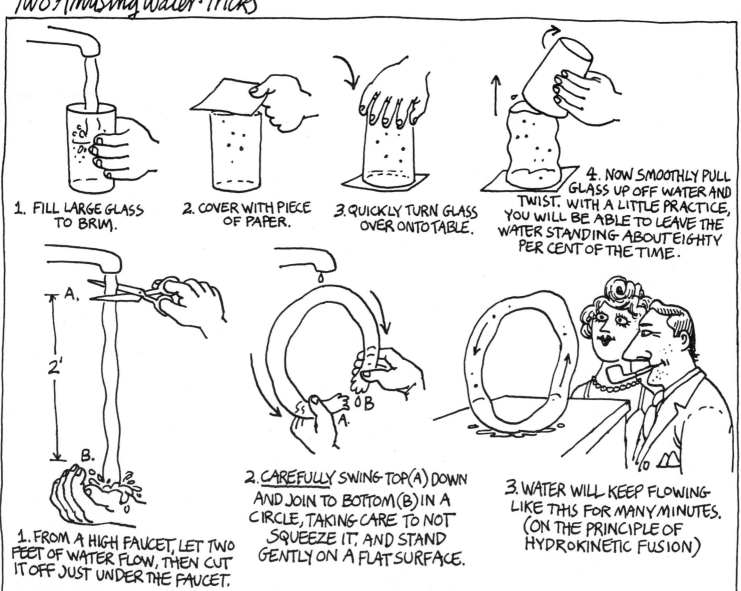

1. FILL LARGE GLASS TO BRIM.

2. COVER WITH PIECE OF PAPER.

3. QUICKLY TURN GLASS OVER ONTO TABLE.

4. NOW SMOOTHLY PULL GLASS UP OFF WATER AND TWIST. WITH A LITTLE PRACTICE, YOU WILL BE ABLE TO LEAVE THE WATER STANDING ABOUT EIGHTY PER CENT OF THE TIME.

A.

2'

B.

1. FROM A HIGH FAUCET, LET TWO FEET OF WATER FLOW, THEN CUT IT OFF JUST UNDER THE FAUCET.

B

A.

2. CAREFULLY SWING TOP (A) DOWN AND JOIN TO BOTTOM (B) IN A CIRCLE, TAKING CARE TO NOT SQUEEZE IT, AND STAND GENTLY ON A FLAT SURFACE.

3. WATER WILL KEEP FLOWING LIKE THIS FOR MANY MINUTES. (ON THE PRINCIPLE OF HYDROKINETIC FUSION)

25

The New World

I'LL HAVE A BONE, A CAT, AND A TENNIS BALL!

28

31

My Dad, the Swimming Champ

29 Caliber Dog Pistol

Tube, the cat

Holding a Cat

Holding 2 cats

41

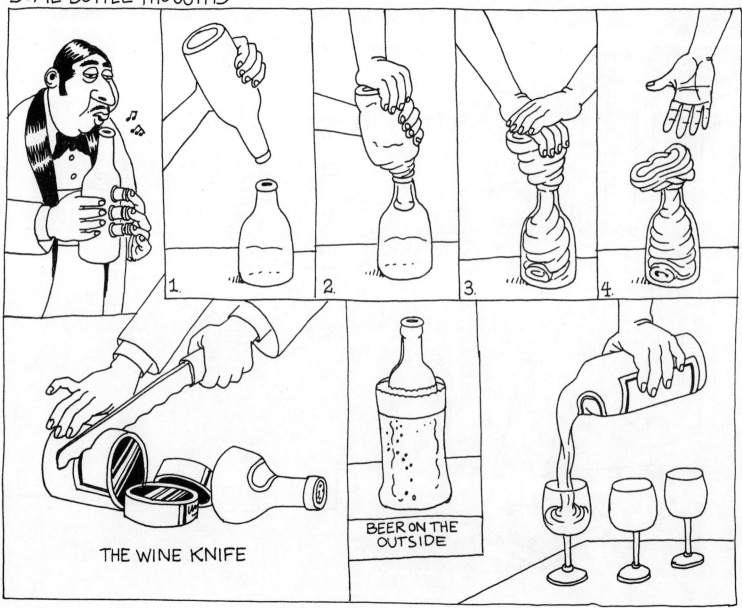

SOME BOTTLE THOUGHTS

1.

2.

3.

4.

THE WINE KNIFE

BEER ON THE OUTSIDE

43

Evil Black Spaghetti

Hostility Toward Matter

Fig. 1

Hostility Toward Art

Fig. 2

Foreign Journalist Injured in Bizarre Happening

FISH DENTIST $3

WATER FOR SALE

50

M-47 MIME PISTOL

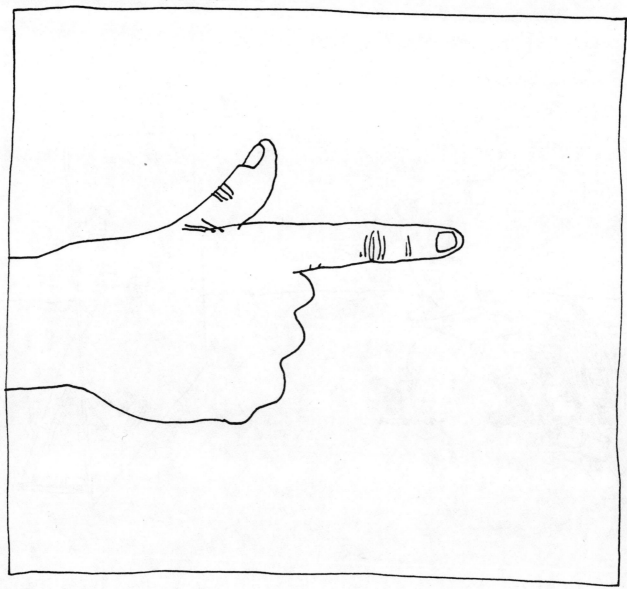

Buzzing Horse

ALARM CLOCK

TWO LARM CLOCKS

57

THE BANANA — SEASONAL VARIATIONS

1.
2.
3.
4.

58

Life on the Pyramids

60

MR. CARROT

Dental Foreplay

College Trained Geek

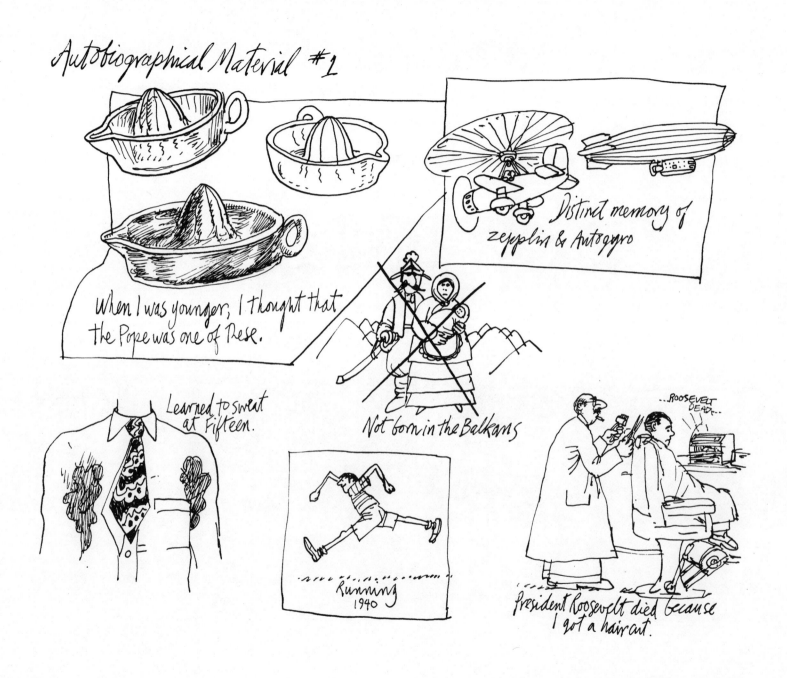

Autobiographical Material #1

When I was younger, I thought that the Pope was one of these.

Distinct memory of zepplin & Autogyro

Not born in the Balkans

Learned to sweat at Fifteen.

Running 1940

...ROOSEVELT DEAD...

President Roosevelt died because I got a haircut.

72

Sweet or Sour Coffee

Peking Cork

Chicken Wings & Rubber Bands

Pieces of Jade

Small Hot Chow Mein

A Thousand Tiny Things with Bacon

Rice

IT WAS A GOOD JOB EXCEPT FOR THE OWLS. RAMONA NEVER LIKED THE OWLS.

6 HATS

INSANE VEGETABLES

HAMLET

CUTLET

PIGLET

ICE SKET

84

What They're Wearing at Court These Days

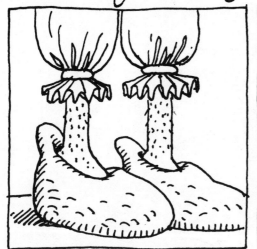

SHOES HANDCARVED
FROM THE FINEST SOAP

SHOULDER CANDLES

A LAPFUL OF FRESH TAR

STYLISH CHICKENSKIN HATS

GRANULAR SHIRT FILLINGS

HEAVILY ARMORED BUTTOCK PLATES

The Museum of Modern Art Butcher Shop

GRAND CHAMPIONS
The Pad Family.

Scratch 'Mom' Pad

Maxi

Mini

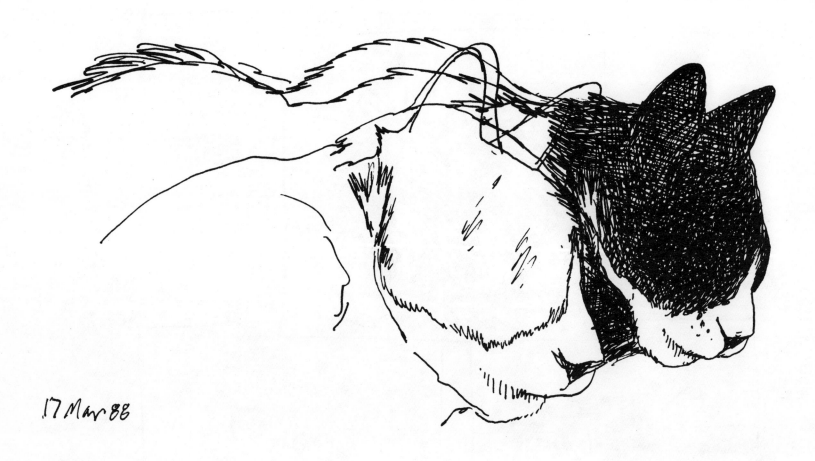

17 Mar 88

94

9 Mar 88

Mini

Mini

Mini

5 Aug 87

95

Luxury Tail

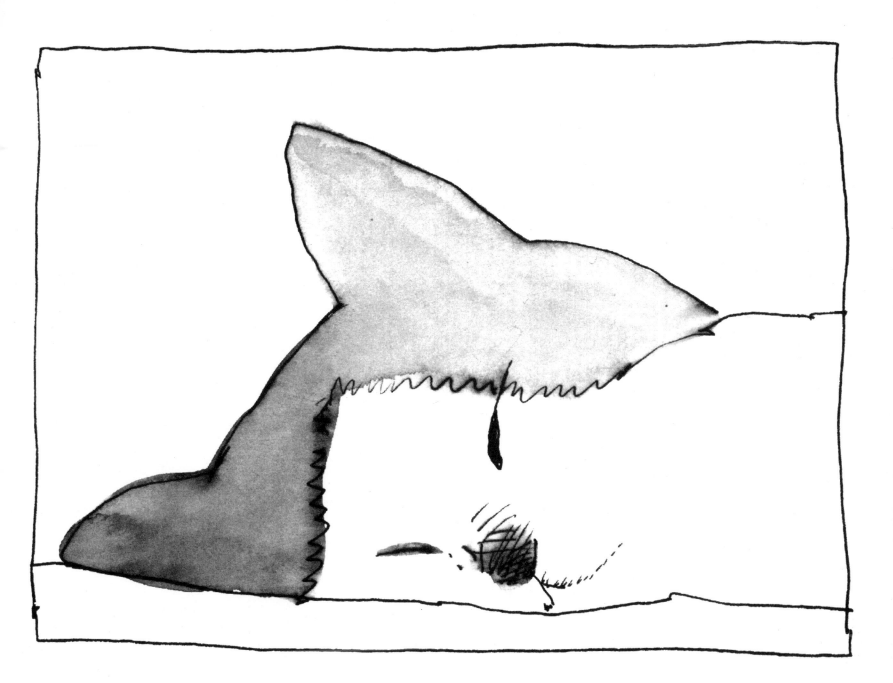

Max

Mini

Max

Mini

Max

Mini

Pie Jumping Cat

Max & Mini

Max & Mini

103

Max & Mini

Max la Mini

105

108

110

111

THE LEGENDARY SOCKS OF WISDOM, APATHY & EQUILIBRIUM

THE AMERICAN REVELATION

122

Inky, The Newspaper Hand Puppet

Mendocino

Life is Just a Bowl

The Pure Energy Chair

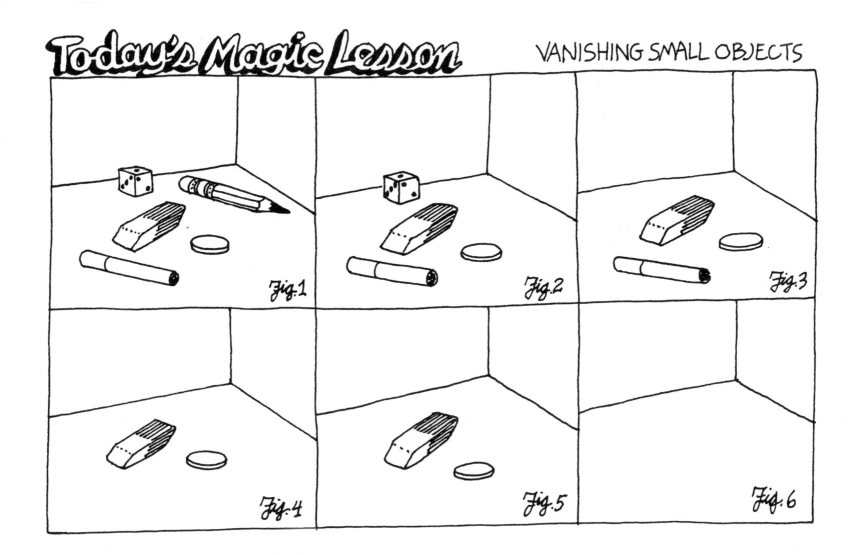

The Tree of Knowledge

137

DECORATOR STRUCK DOWN BY A BOLT OF TASTELESS FABRIC

139

Porcupine Crêpe

ALEXANDER THE GREAT

BARRY THE SHMUCK

THE UMBRELLA CONCEPT ELUDED NORMAN.

THEY DON'T MAKE MIRRORS LIKE THEY USED TO

EITHER.

The Curse

The Conceptual Artist Pours Out His Soul

151

WOMBAT, TOMCAT, KUMQUAT, TOPHAT, PORKBUTT, SLIPKNOT, COLDCUT, TIDBIT

154

155